The First Christmas Song

WRITTEN BY **ALISON BREWIS**

ILLUSTRATED BY **KEZIA HULSE**

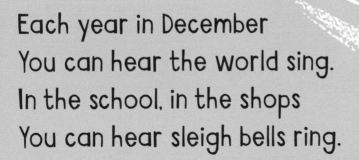

Each year in December
You can hear the world sing.
In the school, in the shops
You can hear sleigh bells ring.

Now listen quite closely
(Or do sing along)
As I tell you the story
Of The First Christmas Song.

It started with Mary,
An ordinary girl,
When she heard some good news
That would change all the world.

An angel said, "Mary,
You're having a son.
He is coming to rescue,
He's God's chosen one."

So Mary
was pregnant

With God's
baby boy!

The news was amazing
So she sang out with joy:

"Glory to God,
He has done a great thing!
He is saving His people
So everyone sing!"

The song kept on growing
And Mary did too,
Until Jesus was born
As a baby brand new.

So God's King arrived
On that first Christmas Day.
And in Bethlehem's manger
He lay in the hay.

The sky filled with angels,
A heavenly throng,

And they joined in the words
Of The First Christmas Song:

"Glory to God,
And to Jesus the King!
He is born as a baby
So everyone sing!"

Then Mary and Joseph
And Jesus so small
Went up to the temple
To thank God for it all.

Simeon lived there,
A very old man.
He trusted in God
And in His rescue plan.

He'd been waiting for Jesus,
He'd waited so long,
Now at last he could join in
The First Christmas Song:

"Glory to God!
I have seen a great thing!
God has kept every promise
So everyone sing!"

So maybe this Christmas
You will hear the world sing.

And over the fields
You might hear church bells ring.

And now that you've heard it
You could sing along.
You could be in the choir
For The First Christmas Song!

Christians sing at Christmas because God kept His promise to send a rescuer. Jesus would grow up to put God's salvation plan into action. He would die on the cross, taking the punishment for our wrongdoing, so that we can be friends with God and enjoy life with Him forever.

We can come to God because of Jesus' rescue and be forgiven for all the wrong things we have done. We just have to ask Him. This good news is worth singing about!

"Glory to God,
He has done a great thing!
He is saving his people
So everyone sing!"

For Nicholas, Ana and Isabelle

The First Christmas Song
Text and Illustrations © 2020 Alison Brewis and Kezia Hulse.

Published by 10Publishing, a division of 10ofThose Limited.
ISBN 978-1-913278-91-5

Typeset by Diane Warnes.

10ofThose Limited, Unit C Tomlinson Road, Leyland, PR25 2DY
Email: info@10ofthose.com   Website: www.10ofthose.com